Time Pieces

for
Horn

Music through the Ages in Two Volumes
for Horn in F or E flat

Volume 2

Selected and arranged by
Paul Harris and Andrew Skirrow

The Associated Board of
the Royal Schools of Music

CONTENTS

Time Pieces for Horn

Volume 2

1728 **First Movement (Triste)** Georg Philipp Telemann
from Bassoon Sonata in F minor (1681–1767)

AB 2842

1749　La réjouissance and La paix

from *Music for the Royal Fireworks*

George Frideric Handel
(1685–1759)

LA RÉJOUISSANCE
Con spirito ♩ = 92

AB 2842

The bracketed trills in the horn part are suggestions only. There are no trills included in the horn parts of Handel's original, but it is quite likely that performers of the period would have played them to match the violin parts.

1775 Contredanse en Rondeau

from Divertimento in F, K. 213

Wolfgang Amadeus Mozart
(1756–1791)

Mozart did not specify any dynamics in the original of this work, a sextet (in F major) for two oboes, two horns and two bassoons. You may like to work out a scheme of dynamics yourself, perhaps using contrasting dynamics on the repeats.

1799 Scherzo and Trio

from Septet Op. 20

Ludwig van Beethoven
(1770–1827)

SCHERZO

Allegro molto e vivace ♩. = 96–112

AB 2842

TRIO

AB 2842

The original Septet (in E♭ major) is for clarinet, bassoon, horn, violin, viola, cello and double bass.

Scherzo D.C.
al Fine

1848 Andante sostenuto

from *50 leçons de chant*, Op. 9

Giuseppe Concone
(1801–1861)

1858 Scherzo and Trio

from Serenade No. 1 in D, Op. 11

Johannes Brahms
(1833–1897)

AB 2842

Fine

TRIO

Scherzo D.C. al Fine

Time Pieces for Horn

Horn in E♭

Volume 2

1728 **First Movement (Triste)**

from Bassoon Sonata in F minor

Georg Philipp Telemann
(1681–1767)

AB 2842

1749 La réjouissance and La paix

from *Music for the Royal Fireworks*

George Frideric Handel
(1685–1759)

The bracketed trills in the horn part are suggestions only. There are no trills included in the horn parts of Handel's original, but it is quite likely that performers of the period would have played them to match the violin parts.

1775 **Contredanse en Rondeau**

from Divertimento in F, K. 213

Wolfgang Amadeus Mozart
(1756–1791)

Molto allegro ♩ = 144

Mozart did not specify any dynamics in the Original of this work, a sextet (in F major) for two oboes, two horns and two bassoons. You may like to work out a scheme of dynamics yourself, perhaps using contrasting dynamics on the repeats.

1799 Scherzo and Trio

from Septet Op. 20

Ludwig Van Beethoven
(1770–1827)

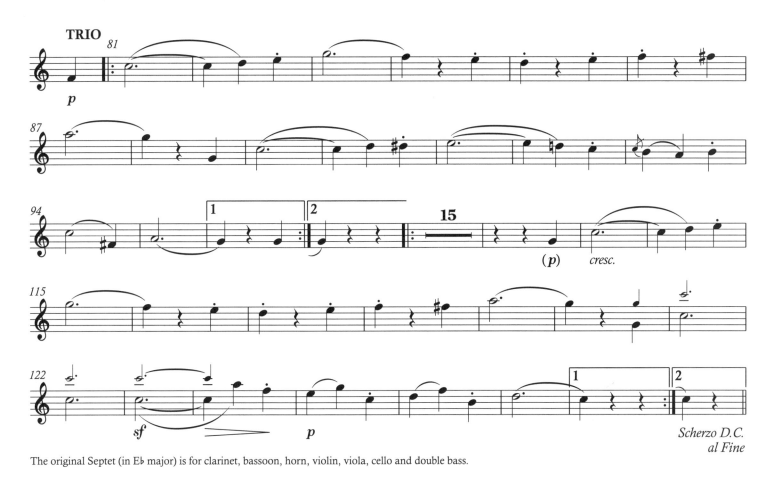

TRIO

The original Septet (in E♭ major) is for clarinet, bassoon, horn, violin, viola, cello and double bass.

Scherzo D.C.
al Fine

1848   Andante sostenuto

from *50 leçons de chant*, Op. 9

Giuseppe Concone
(1801–1861)

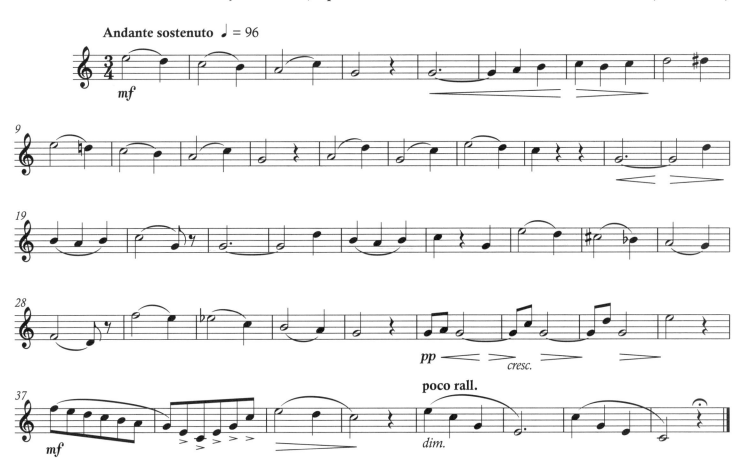

Andante sostenuto ♩ = 96

poco rall.

1858 Scherzo and Trio

from Serenade No. 1 in D, Op. 11

Johannes Brahms
(1833–1897)

AB 2842

1874 Romance
Op. 36

Camille Saint-Saëns
(1835–1921)

1889 **Ballet**

from *Petite suite*

Claude Debussy
(1862–1918)

1893 **Evening Prayer**
from *Hänsel und Gretel*

Engelbert Humperdinck
(1854–1921)

1951 Aria
Op. 14 No. 1

Iain Hamilton
(1922–2000)

With its long, wide-arching melody and syncopated rhythms, this original composition for horn and piano is typical of this Scottish composer's music. Notice, also, the chromaticism and use of all 12 pitches in the melody, not least in the first six bars. By 1955 (in his *Three Piano Pieces*), Hamilton had adopted serialism and the 12-note technique as found in the works of Schoenberg and Webern.

AB 2842

1965 Psalm 23

from *Chichester Psalms*

Leonard Bernstein
(1918–1990)

Adapted by Paul Harris and Andrew Skirrow after the arrangement by David Elliot.

2002 Arioso for Albert

from *Bermuda Suite and Dolphin*

Gary Carpenter
(b. 1951)

Printed in England by Caligraving Ltd, Thetford, Norfolk

Music origination by
Barnes Music Engraving Ltd, East Sussex

AB 2842

Time Pieces for Horn

Horn in F

Volume 2

1728 # First Movement (Triste)

from Bassoon Sonata in F minor

Georg Philipp Telemann
(1681–1767)

AB 2842

1749 La réjouissance and La paix

from *Music for the Royal Fireworks*

George Frideric Handel
(1685–1759)

The bracketed trills in the horn part are suggestions only. There are no trills included in the horn parts of Handel's original, but it is quite likely that performers of the period would have played them to match the violin parts.

1775 **Contredanse en Rondeau**
from Divertimento in F, K. 213

Wolfgang Amadeus Mozart
(1756–1791)

Mozart did not specify any dynamics in the Original of this work, a sextet (in F major) for two oboes, two horns and two bassoons. You may like to work out a scheme of dynamics yourself, perhaps using contrasting dynamics on the repeats.

1799 Scherzo and Trio

from Septet Op. 20

Ludwig Van Beethoven
(1770–1827)

AB 2842

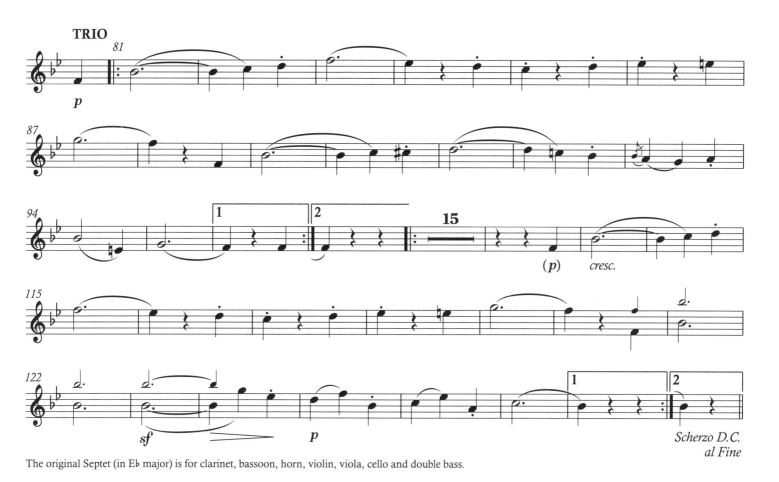

The original Septet (in E♭ major) is for clarinet, bassoon, horn, violin, viola, cello and double bass.

1848 **Andante sostenuto**
from *50 leçons de chant*, Op. 9

Giuseppe Concone
(1801–1861)

1858 Scherzo and Trio

from Serenade No. 1 in D, Op. 11

Johannes Brahms
(1833–1897)

AB 2842

1874 Romance
Op. 36

Camille Saint-Saëns
(1835–1921)

1889 Ballet

from *Petite suite*

Claude Debussy
(1862–1918)

AB 2842

1893 **Evening Prayer**
from *Hänsel und Gretel*

Engelbert Humperdinck
(1854–1921)

1951 Aria
Op. 14 No. 1

Iain Hamilton
(1922–2000)

With its long, wide-arching melody and syncopated rhythms, this original composition for horn and piano is typical of this Scottish composer's music. Notice, also, the chromaticism and use of all 12 pitches in the melody, not least in the first six bars. By 1955 (in his *Three Piano Pieces*), Hamilton had adopted serialism and the 12-note technique as found in the works of Schoenberg and Webern.

AB 2842

1965 Psalm 23

from *Chichester Psalms*

Leonard Bernstein
(1918–1990)

2002 **Arioso for Albert**

from *Bermuda Suite and Dolphin*

Gary Carpenter
(b. 1951)

Printed in England by Caligraving Ltd, Thetford, Norfolk

Music origination by
Barnes Music Engraving Ltd, East Sussex

AB 2842

1874 Romance

Op. 36

Camille Saint-Saëns
(1835–1921)

Un peu plus de mouvt

1889 Ballet

from *Petite suite*

Claude Debussy
(1862–1918)

to Coda ⊕

Tempo di valse

poco rit.

a tempo

Tempo I

D.S. al Coda

AB 2842

1893 Evening Prayer

from *Hänsel und Gretel*

Engelbert Humperdinck
(1854–1921)

1951 Aria

Op. 14 No. 1

Iain Hamilton
(1922–2000)

AB 2842

With its long, wide-arching melody and syncopated rhythms, this original composition for horn and piano is typical of this Scottish composer's music. Notice, also, the chromaticism and use of all 12 pitches in the melody, not least in the first six bars. By 1955 (in his *Three Piano Pieces*), Hamilton had adopted serialism and the 12-note technique as found in the works of Schoenberg and Webern.

1965 Psalm 23

from *Chichester Psalms*

Leonard Bernstein
(1918–1990)

AB 2842

2002   Arioso for Albert

from *Bermuda Suite and Dolphin*

Gary Carpenter
(b. 1951)

Printed in England by Caligraving Ltd, Thetford, Norfolk

Music origination by
Barnes Music Engraving Ltd, East Sussex